Swear Word Coloring Book

Deluxe Edition

Colormom Books

Visit www.colormom.com For Free Printable Adult Coloring Pages

ISBN: 978-1-944575-40-3

Printed in the U.S.A

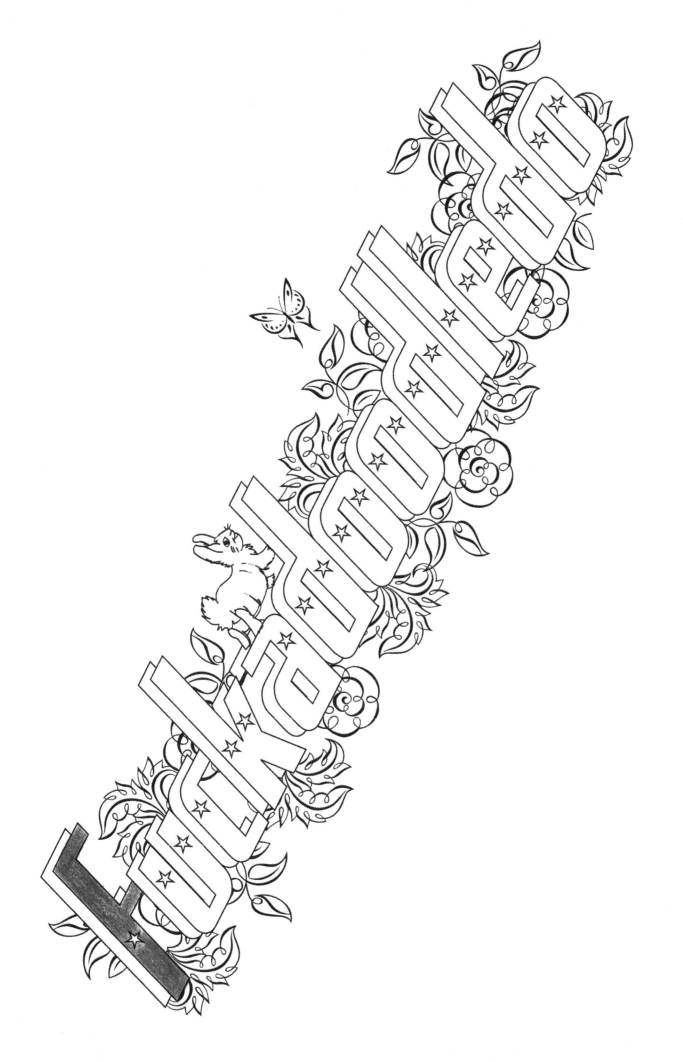

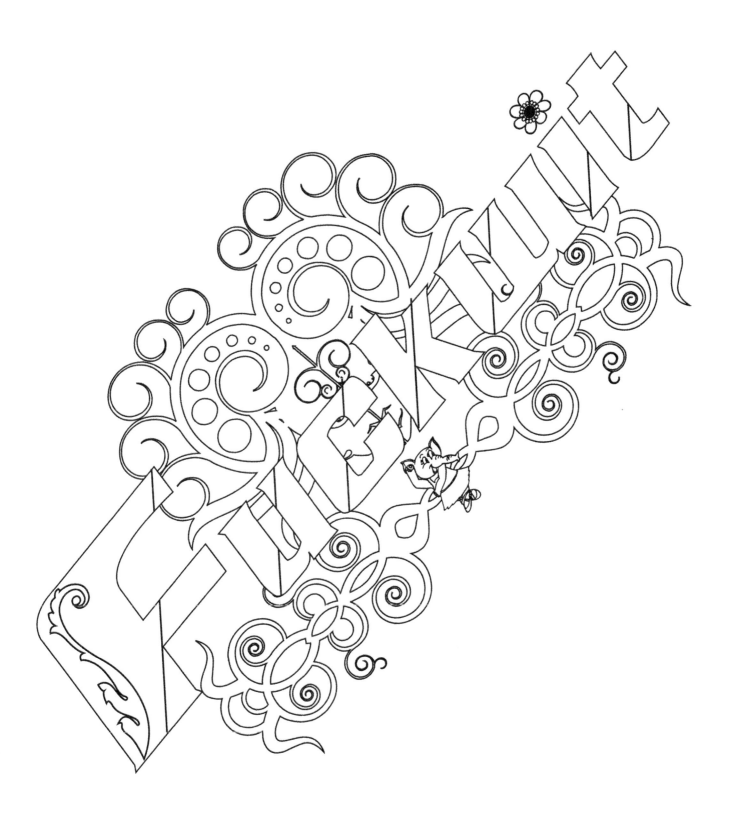

Thank You

If you enjoyed Coloring this Fancy Swears, please take a little time to share your thoughts and post a positive review with 5 star rating on Amazon, it would encourage me and make me serve you better. It'd Really be greatly appreciated.

We'll never be perfect, but that won't stop us from trying. Your feedback makes us serve you better. Send ideas, criticism, Compliment or anything else you think we should hear to info@colormom.com. We'll Reply you As soon as we receive your Mail. :)

Also, Don't Forget to visit **www.swearwordscoloring.com**

For Free Printable Coloring Pages Every Week!

Visit our Author Page to get More Amazing Adults Coloring

Facebook Page here>> https://www.facebook.com/swearwordscoloring/

CPSIA information can be obtained
at www.ICGtesting.com
Printed in the USA
BVOW10s2331031117

499542BV00012B/569/P